My VOLLEYBALL *Season*

A journal of my skills,
my matches, and my memories.

Karleen Tauszik

TIP
TOP
BOOKS

Published by Tip Top Books, Dunedin, Florida

Summary: This journal provides children with a place to track their volleyball season: their matches, practices, areas of improvement and contribution, and their fun memories.

ISBN: 978-1-954130-11-1

Karleen Tauszik is the author of books for children ages 8-12. Visit her on the web at KarleenT.com, where you can see her other books and sign up for her newsletter.

This book belongs to

_____

My Volleyball Season

from _____ to _____
             Date   Date

Hurrah! You're on the team!

This journal is the perfect place to track your volleyball season—your practice sessions, your matches, the highlights of the season, and all the fun you'll have.

Here's what you'll find inside:

First, there are six pages to journal your pre-season weeks of practice.

Next, there are enough pages to journal up to 16 matches, so you have enough for any pre-season matches, the main season, and a few for tournaments. Need more? One is reserved for photocopying.

In between each match page, you'll find a page to journal how your practice sessions are going.

At the end, there are seven blank pages to fill with photos, extra notes, statistics, and mementos. You can even get all your teammates to write notes and their autographs if you like. Add whatever you want to so you remember your volleyball season and make this book uniquely yours.

Good luck and have a great season!

Pre-Season Practice

The week starting _____

Day & Date

Coach's focus this week is: _____

_____

_____

My focus this week is: _____

_____

_____

How I feel starting out: _____

_____

_____

What I think I can contribute to the team this week: ___

_____

_____

My notes about this week's practice: _____

_____

_____

_____

_____

_____

_____

_____

Pre-Season Practice

The week starting _____

Coach's focus this week is: _____
_____

_____

My focus this week is: _____
_____

_____

How I feel starting out: _____
_____

_____

What I think I can contribute to the team this week: _____
_____

_____

My notes about this week's practice: _____
_____

_____

_____

_____

_____

_____

_____

Pre-Season Practice

The week starting _____

Coach's focus this week is: _____

_____

_____

My focus this week is: _____

_____

_____

How I feel starting out: _____

_____

_____

What I think I can contribute to the team this week: _____

_____

_____

My notes about this week's practice: _____

_____

_____

_____

_____

_____

_____

_____

Pre-Season Practice

The week starting _____

Coach's focus this week is: _____

_____

_____

My focus this week is: _____

_____

_____

How I feel starting out: _____

_____

_____

What I think I can contribute to the team this week: _____

_____

_____

My notes about this week's practice: _____

_____

_____

_____

_____

_____

_____

_____

Pre-Season Practice

The week starting _____

Coach's focus this week is: _____

_____

_____

My focus this week is: _____

_____

_____

How I feel starting out: _____

_____

_____

What I think I can contribute to the team this week: _____

_____

_____

My notes about this week's practice: _____

_____

_____

_____

_____

_____

_____

_____

Pre-Season Practice

The week starting _____
Day & Date

Coach's focus this week is: _____
_____
_____

My focus this week is: _____
_____
_____

How I feel starting out: _____
_____
_____

What I think I can contribute to the team this week: ____
_____
_____

My notes about this week's practice: _____
_____
_____
_____
_____
_____
_____
_____

Match Day

Match Date: _____ Match Time: _____

We played against: _____ Home ☐   Away ☐

Final Score: _____

My summary: _____

_____

_____

_____

Coach's comments: _____

_____

_____

My contributions: _____

_____

_____

_____

What I could have done better: _____

_____

_____

_____

Highlights of the match: _____

_____

_____

_____

_____

_____

Practice

Starting _____ until our next match on _____

                    Day & Date   Day & Date

Coach's focus this week is: _____

_____

_____

My focus this week is: _____

_____

_____

How I feel looking ahead: _____

_____

_____

What I think I can contribute to the team this week: _____

_____

_____

My notes about this week's practice: _____

_____

_____

_____

_____

_____

_____

_____

Match Day

Match Date: _____   Match Time: _____

We played against: _____   Home ☐   Away ☐

Final Score: _____

My summary: _____
_____
_____
_____

Coach's comments: _____
_____
_____

My contributions: _____
_____
_____
_____

What I could have done better: _____
_____
_____
_____

Highlights of the match: _____
_____
_____
_____
_____
_____

Practice

Starting _____ until our next match on _____

Coach's focus this week is: _____

_____

_____

My focus this week is: _____

_____

_____

How I feel looking ahead: _____

_____

_____

What I think I can contribute to the team this week: _____

_____

_____

My notes about this week's practice: _____

_____

_____

_____

_____

_____

_____

_____

Match Day

Match Date: _____   Match Time: _____

We played against: _____   Home ☐   Away ☐

Final Score: _____

My summary: _____
_____
_____
_____

Coach's comments: _____
_____
_____

My contributions: _____
_____
_____
_____

What I could have done better: _____
_____
_____
_____

Highlights of the match: _____
_____
_____
_____
_____
_____

Practice

Starting _____ until our next match on _____

                                                      Day & Date

Coach's focus this week is: _____

_____

_____

My focus this week is: _____

_____

_____

How I feel looking ahead: _____

_____

_____

What I think I can contribute to the team this week: _____

_____

_____

My notes about this week's practice: _____

_____

_____

_____

_____

_____

_____

_____

_____

Match Day

Match Date: _____ Match Time: _____

We played against: _____ Home ☐ Away ☐

Final Score: _____

My summary: _____
_____
_____
_____

Coach's comments: _____
_____
_____

My contributions: _____
_____
_____

What I could have done better: _____
_____
_____

Highlights of the match: _____
_____
_____
_____
_____
_____

Practice

Starting _____ until our next match on _____
  Day & Date   Day & Date

Coach's focus this week is: _____

_____

_____

My focus this week is: _____

_____

_____

How I feel looking ahead: _____

_____

_____

What I think I can contribute to the team this week: _____

_____

_____

My notes about this week's practice: _____

_____

_____

_____

_____

_____

_____

_____

Match Day

Match Date: _____   Match Time: _____

We played against: _____   Home ☐   Away ☐

Final Score: _____

My summary: _____
_____
_____
_____

Coach's comments: _____
_____
_____

My contributions: _____
_____
_____
_____

What I could have done better: _____
_____
_____
_____

Highlights of the match: _____
_____
_____
_____
_____
_____

Practice

Starting _____ until our next match on _____

Day & Date   Day & Date

Coach's focus this week is: _____

_____

_____

My focus this week is: _____

_____

_____

How I feel looking ahead: _____

_____

_____

What I think I can contribute to the team this week: _____

_____

_____

My notes about this week's practice: _____

_____

_____

_____

_____

_____

_____

_____

_____

Match Day

Match Date: _____ Match Time: _____

We played against: _____ Home ☐ Away ☐

Final Score: _____

My summary: _____
_____
_____

Coach's comments: _____
_____

My contributions: _____
_____
_____

What I could have done better: _____
_____
_____

Highlights of the match: _____
_____
_____
_____
_____

Practice

Starting _____ until our next match on _____
                Day & Date   Day & Date

Coach's focus this week is: _____

_____

_____

My focus this week is: _____

_____

_____

How I feel looking ahead: _____

_____

_____

What I think I can contribute to the team this week: _____

_____

_____

My notes about this week's practice: _____

_____

_____

_____

_____

_____

_____

_____

Match Day

Match Date: _____   Match Time: _____

We played against: _____   Home ☐   Away ☐

Final Score: _____

My summary: _____

_____

_____

_____

Coach's comments: _____

_____

_____

My contributions: _____

_____

_____

What I could have done better: _____

_____

_____

Highlights of the match: _____

_____

_____

_____

_____

_____

Practice

Starting _____ until our next match on _____
          Day & Date   Day & Date

Coach's focus this week is: _____

_____

_____

My focus this week is: _____

_____

_____

How I feel looking ahead: _____

_____

_____

What I think I can contribute to the team this week: _____

_____

_____

My notes about this week's practice: _____

_____

_____

_____

_____

_____

_____

_____

_____

Match Day

Match Date: _____   Match Time: _____

We played against: _____   Home ☐   Away ☐

Final Score: _____

My summary: _____

_____

_____

_____

Coach's comments: _____

_____

_____

My contributions: _____

_____

_____

_____

What I could have done better: _____

_____

_____

Highlights of the match: _____

_____

_____

_____

_____

Practice

Starting _____ until our next match on _____
Day & Date Day & Date

Coach's focus this week is: _____

_____

_____

My focus this week is: _____

_____

_____

How I feel looking ahead: _____

_____

_____

What I think I can contribute to the team this week: _____

_____

_____

My notes about this week's practice: _____

_____

_____

_____

_____

_____

_____

_____

Match Day

Match Date: _____   Match Time: _____

We played against: _____   Home ☐   Away ☐

Final Score: _____

My summary: _____
_____
_____
_____

Coach's comments: _____
_____
_____

My contributions: _____
_____
_____
_____

What I could have done better: _____
_____
_____
_____

Highlights of the match: _____
_____
_____
_____
_____
_____

Practice

Starting _____ until our next match on _____
                         Day & Date   Day & Date

Coach's focus this week is: _____

_____

My focus this week is: _____

_____

How I feel looking ahead: _____

_____

What I think I can contribute to the team this week: _____

_____

My notes about this week's practice: _____

_____

_____

_____

_____

_____

_____

_____

Match Day

Match Date: _____ Match Time: _____

We played against: _____ Home ☐   Away ☐

Final Score: _____

My summary: _____

_____

_____

_____

Coach's comments: _____

_____

_____

My contributions: _____

_____

_____

_____

What I could have done better: _____

_____

_____

_____

Highlights of the match: _____

_____

_____

_____

_____

_____

Practice

Starting _____ until our next match on _____
          Day & Date   Day & Date

Coach's focus this week is: _____

_____

_____

My focus this week is: _____

_____

_____

How I feel looking ahead: _____

_____

_____

What I think I can contribute to the team this week: _____

_____

_____

My notes about this week's practice: _____

_____

_____

_____

_____

_____

_____

_____

Match Day

Match Date: _____ Match Time: _____

We played against: _____ Home ☐   Away ☐

Final Score: _____

My summary: _____

_____

_____

_____

Coach's comments: _____

_____

_____

My contributions: _____

_____

_____

_____

What I could have done better: _____

_____

_____

Highlights of the match: _____

_____

_____

_____

_____

_____

Practice

Starting _____ until our next match on _____
             Day & Date   Day & Date

Coach's focus this week is: _____

_____

My focus this week is: _____

_____

How I feel looking ahead: _____

_____

What I think I can contribute to the team this week: _____

_____

My notes about this week's practice: _____

_____

_____

_____

_____

_____

_____

_____

Match Day

Match Date: _____   Match Time: _____

We played against: _____   Home ☐   Away ☐

Final Score: _____

My summary: _____

_____

_____

_____

Coach's comments: _____

_____

_____

My contributions: _____

_____

_____

_____

What I could have done better: _____

_____

_____

_____

Highlights of the match: _____

_____

_____

_____

_____

_____

Practice

Starting _____ until our next match on _____
   <small>Day & Date</small>   <small>Day & Date</small>

Coach's focus this week is: _____

_____

_____

My focus this week is: _____

_____

_____

How I feel looking ahead: _____

_____

_____

What I think I can contribute to the team this week: _____

_____

_____

My notes about this week's practice: _____

_____

_____

_____

_____

_____

_____

_____

Match Day

Match Date: _____   Match Time: _____

We played against: _____   Home ☐   Away ☐

Final Score: _____

My summary: _____

_____

_____

_____

Coach's comments: _____

_____

_____

My contributions: _____

_____

_____

_____

What I could have done better: _____

_____

_____

_____

Highlights of the match: _____

_____

_____

_____

_____

_____

Practice

Starting _____ until our next match on _____

Coach's focus this week is: _____

_____

_____

My focus this week is: _____

_____

_____

How I feel looking ahead: _____

_____

_____

What I think I can contribute to the team this week: _____

_____

_____

My notes about this week's practice: _____

_____

_____

_____

_____

_____

_____

_____

Match Day

Match Date: _____ Match Time: _____

We played against: _____ Home ☐ Away ☐

Final Score: _____

My summary: _____

_____

_____

_____

Coach's comments: _____

_____

_____

My contributions: _____

_____

_____

_____

What I could have done better: _____

_____

_____

_____

Highlights of the match: _____

_____

_____

_____

_____

_____

Practice

Starting _____ until our next match on _____
Day & Date Day & Date

Coach's focus this week is: _____

_____

_____

My focus this week is: _____

_____

_____

How I feel looking ahead: _____

_____

_____

What I think I can contribute to the team this week: _____

_____

_____

My notes about this week's practice: _____

_____

_____

_____

_____

_____

_____

_____

_____

Match Day

Match Date: _____   Match Time: _____

We played against: _____   Home ☐   Away ☐

Final Score: _____

My summary: _____

_____

_____

_____

Coach's comments: _____

_____

_____

My contributions: _____

_____

_____

_____

What I could have done better: _____

_____

_____

_____

Highlights of the match: _____

_____

_____

_____

_____

_____

Practice

Starting _____ until our next match on _____

Day & Date   Day & Date

Coach's focus this week is: _____

_____

_____

My focus this week is: _____

_____

_____

How I feel looking ahead: _____

_____

_____

What I think I can contribute to the team this week: _____

_____

_____

My notes about this week's practice: _____

_____

_____

_____

_____

_____

_____

_____

Match Day

Match Date: _____   Match Time: _____

We played against: _____   Home ☐   Away ☐

Final Score: _____

My summary: _____

_____

_____

_____

Coach's comments: _____

_____

_____

My contributions: _____

_____

_____

_____

What I could have done better: _____

_____

_____

Highlights of the match: _____

_____

_____

_____

_____

Practice

Starting _____ until our next match on _____
Day & Date   Day & Date

Coach's focus this week is: _____

_____

_____

My focus this week is: _____

_____

_____

How I feel looking ahead: _____

_____

_____

What I think I can contribute to the team this week: _____

_____

_____

My notes about this week's practice: _____

_____

_____

_____

_____

_____

_____

_____

_____

What a season you've had!

You've used up 16 of your

worksheet sets.

There's one more after this page.

Use it to make as many

photocopies as you need

to complete your season.

Match Day

Match Date: _____ Match Time: _____

We played against: _____ Home ☐   Away ☐

Final Score: _____

My summary: _____

_____

_____

_____

Coach's comments: _____

_____

_____

My contributions: _____

_____

_____

_____

What I could have done better: _____

_____

_____

_____

Highlights of the match: _____

_____

_____

_____

_____

_____

Practice

Starting _____ until our next match on _____
Day & Date   Day & Date

Coach's focus this week is: _____

_____

_____

My focus this week is: _____

_____

_____

How I feel looking ahead: _____

_____

_____

What I think I can contribute to the team this week: _____

_____

_____

My notes about this week's practice: _____

_____

_____

_____

_____

_____

_____

_____

_____

My
VOLLEYBALL
Season
Memories

Memories

Memories

Memories

Memories

About the Author

Karleen Tauszik writes books mostly for children ages 8 to 12. Her goal as an author is to get kids to LOVE reading. She is married to a professional ventriloquist and magician, and they live in the Tampa Bay area.

Interested in other sports? Look for the rest of the "My Season" Journals:

My Baseball Season

My Softball Season

My Soccer Season

My Hockey Season

My Basketball Season

My Football Season

My Cheerleading Season

Learn more about Karleen and her other books at her website, KarleenT.com. Ask a parent to sign up for her newsletter so you'll be the first to know about new books.

Made in the USA
Monee, IL
10 November 2021